ABOUT THE AUTHOR

Holly Jackson was born in North Wales and has lived all over the UK, including Berkshire and the Lake District. She now lives in County Durham and works as a teaching assistant for children with additional needs. Holly has been writing poetry and short fiction for over twenty years and her work has appeared in *Fragmented Voices, MumWrite, Poet Versus*, Analog Submission Press, *Periwinkle Lit Mag, Skirting Around Magazine* and others. You can find her on Instagram at @hjacksonwrites.

Banana and Salted Caramel is Holly Jackson's debut collection.

Holly Jackson

BANANA AND SALTED CARAMEL

A Collection of Poetry and Short Stories

AUSTIN MACAULEY PUBLISHERS™

LONDON • CAMBRIDGE • NEW YORK • SHARJAH

A CIP catalogue record for this title is available from the British
Library.

ISBN 9781528997409 (Paperback)
ISBN 9781528997416 (ePub e-book)

www.austinmacauley.com

First Published 2022
Austin Macauley Publishers Ltd
1 Canada Square
Canary Wharf
London
E14 5AA

DEDICATIONS

To Max – because I always keep my promises.

To the love of my life: my daughter – who grants me daily
love, laughter, fun, motivation and fodder.

For Melanie – who was always prouder of me than I deserved.

ACKNOWLEDGEMENTS

Thanks to several of my friends and family who've given their time to be used as guinea pigs for my feedback.

To the team at Austin Macauley, thank you for all your hard work and help through the publishing process.

And thank you to my friend and neighbour Hannah, whose proofreading efforts have never earned her a single penny.

CONTENTS

SHORT STORIES

POETRY

If I Could Have a Year

If I could have a year, I'd spend it running,
In any direction South of here.
If I could have a year, I'd spend it living,
In any place apart from here.

If I could have a year, I'd travel far; to the City line,
And find a place that I'd call mine.
I'd make it on my own domain,
To see if I still could again.

If I could have a year, I'd spend it loving,
Someone else apart from him.
Be with a woman, just to know how it would feel,
And fall in love with my own skin.

If I could have a year, I'd run from this job,
This never-ending non career.
To sit in parks and fields, and write for all my life,
Even if only for the birds to hear.

I'd do anything else,
If I had a year, I'd do it all.
No responsibilities, no broken bones or hearts,
Just life, mine for one year.

But once the wind grew cold,
And the leaves had gone their way.
I'd end my year back in the home I'd known,
Never again to stray.

For I'd only need one year,
To know that life exits.
To learn what I was missing,
And take some different twists.

Then once my year was done,
I'd return to my life here today.
Into his arms, oh how I would run,
Forever then to stay.

Hopes & Dreams

Hopes & dreams are fleeting things, they change day by day.
But when our dreams go unfulfilled, our hearts are filled with pain.
A secret fear fills our souls, questions start to creep.
When we're worried things won't change, a wound emerges deep.
When will I have the things I crave?
A happy home?
A child of my own?
These things I have in a box in my heart, locked away and safe.

But when my mind is heavy laden, with doubts about my future,
I confide in you, my dearest friend, my notebook, pen & paper.
I tell you all my heart's desires, things I fear will never be.
Will this finger always be bare?
Will there ever be a little me?
One day I'll see my wishes granted, of this I'm almost sure.
But then, of course, new wishes will force
their way into the fold.

Will my child do well in life?
Will I travel when I'm old?
We humans are a fickle breed,
always wishing for fulfilling need.
So, let me for now forget my laments,
have patience & be happy within life's moments.

Roller Coaster

(The first poem I ever wrote, around fourteen years old)

You to me are a white-knuckle ride,
my very own Roller Coaster deep inside.
Deep love one day, raging anger the next,
you bring out everything, my worst and my best.

When I think of you, I get butterflies,
when I hear your voice, I touch the skies.
When I see your smile, I melt away.
You touch me and my whole world shakes.

You've made me cry so many times,
but what's always more are the times I've smiled.
You and I are friends, the best forever,
but I wish you were more; my love, my lover.
When I think of you, I get butterflies,

when I hear your voice, I touch the skies.
When I see your smile, I melt away.
You touch me and my whole world shakes.

You make me doubt my beliefs of love,
you make me think you're way above.
My feelings for you make my head spin 'round.
If I didn't know better, I'd think love was found.

Beautiful and Happy

Here I sit, on the sofa, reading,
drinking tea and eating a chocolate orange.
(The centre is my favourite, I always leave it till last.)
You're drinking wine and playing on the PlayStation,
my feet are resting in your lap, your wrists are resting on my feet.
No one speaks; there's not need.
(It's a comfortable silence.)
In a while we'll go to bed,
we might make love (if we're not too tired).
Tomorrow we might go to the supermarket, or the garden centre.
(Or do nothing, that's more likely.)

One day, one of us will die
and leave the other,
to read and shop and rest alone.
(But we don't talk about that.)
Sometimes we walk in the countryside.
When we can afford it, we have a holiday.
We don't change the world
(just each other's).
That's what life is:

like the flowers in the meadow,
swaying in the breeze.
Not doing anything special,
just living.
(Doing the same thing every day.)
Beautiful,
and happy.

I Fear for You

I worry about you, *already*.
Even though we have never met,
I fear for you.
I will do my very best,
but what if my best is not enough?

One day you will be grown
and I will no longer be the one you trust.
I must allow you to make your own mistakes.
How can I prepare you for all that you will face?
When I barely know how to prepare myself for this world.

If you are a girl, how will I teach you,
to be strong, fierce, independent, loving and open?
How will I teach you to navigate this cruel, intolerant world,
which prizes beauty over kindness, breasts over brains?
How will I teach you to make your way through all this and find *you*
  on the other side?

If you are a boy, how will I teach you
to be kind, to be loving, respectful and gentle?
How can I convince you that it is no sin to be sweet?
To weep, to smell the roses and see the beauty in the sunrise?
How do you teach a gentle heart and a strong head?

How will I teach you to be strong, without becoming hard?
How can I teach you to be honest rather than naïve?
You are not even a part of me yet,
I worry you may never be and I long for it.
Then I look at the world around me and wonder if you even should.

Sometimes, *like now*, all I see is hate, fear,
intolerance, prejudice, anger and hardship.
This world is a stagnant swamp and it's only getting worse.
Yet selfishly I ache for you to join it,
though I fear for you if you do.
There is no answer to this question.
There is no conclusion in this poem.

The Secret

She has a secret she'll never reveal,
not to her friends, or the one: her ideal.
This secret she keeps, never to share,
hidden too deep, ever to bare.

It's hers alone, her burden to hide,
no-one else knows what she keeps inside.
This part of herself, her refusal to share,
it's not what *you'd* think, she never would care.

This secret she keeps, in a heart of oak,
it's hers alone, her own private joke.
She says, "It's between myself and I...
Not a soul will suspect, that I live in this lie."

This secret desire shall burn ever deeper.
Though she'll never succumb, your love it will keep her.
But at night whilst dreaming, she has no more chains,
in sweetness of slumber, no consequence remains.

You could never understand, this part of her being,
it's inconsequential, there's no need in seeing.
She is not ashamed, she hides not for fears,
her secret is simply something that's hers.

This side of herself, she'll never explore,
unless the day comes, she needs you no more.
And even if this would ever be true,
it could never be shared with other than you.

It's the one piece of herself she keeps for her own,
while everything else she shares with the throngs.

But you'll know of no secret,
you'll never suspect,
this poem remains forever unread.

Life and Death Summed up in Haiku

I like to walk through graveyards,
strolling happily amongst the peaceful dead.
Wondering about lives once lived.
Some whole families resting in one place,
departed decades apart, reunited in kind death.

Others over a century passed,
entirely forgotten, but for now, visited by this odd stranger.
Reading epitaphs, a few short lines meant to sum up a whole life.
History etched in stone, saying so much more than its mere words.
Like a haiku.

I wonder about you, your years condensed on this stone.
What did you look like?
Did you enjoy the taste of Marmite? The smell of fresh cut grass?
Did you just do the best you could?
Were you happy?

I wonder, if one hundred years from now,
some odd stranger will visit me.
And wonder…
Care…
Read my death haiku.

H. Jackson lies here,
she enjoyed indie music,
hated Marmite. Lived.

Photographs of People I Don't Know

In my home,
in the albums on my shelves,
there are photographs
of people I do not know.

Old dusty pictures,
worn and sepia brown,
of people I have never known,
or at least do not remember.

Old friends of family passed,
living forever on this page,
parties in my childhood,
with guests I cannot name.

But on my shelves they stay, ever to remain.
For it seems a sin to throw away
a memory, a frame in time,
someone's life connected with mine.

For perhaps somewhere there are pictures of me;
in a home,
in the albums on the shelves,
of people I do not know.

Brain Freeze

I have forgotten a word,
I'm posting a comment online.
A quick thesis, in response to some doylum with stupid opinions.
But I have forgotten a word…

I write some more,
what *is* that word?
I wrack my brain,
It's in there somewhere…
nothing.

I try to recall, when I've used it before.
It's on the tip of my tongue,
well not the tip actually, maybe a little further back… the root in
   fact.
Never mind, it'll come to me…
nothing.

I write some more,
what *is* that word?
Still nothing.
This word would make my point…
nothing.

I go to Google for the answer,
type in something familiar.
Scroll through lists of synonyms,
and antonyms. Just in case…
nothing.

I begin to doubt myself.
Does this word even exist?
Never mind, just keep writing.
This word would *make* my point…
still nothing.

Give up,
post comment…
…
still nothing…
…

Three days later,
watching TV.
Someone says the word…
It was *'manipulative'*.

I'm Sorry

I forgot you.
It happens all the time.
I love you and leave you to rest, on a shelf, alone.
Someone told me: "You think of people all the time, what's in a day?"
But I don't.
I forget you all the time. Except on those days, when I give myself
  permission to remember.
Except… This time I didn't.

But you remember me, even now I can feel you here, watching.
Your love burns a pit in my stomach.
A hot, tight knot of guilt and judgement.
But I know, that's just how you love me.
It's how you always did.
Love with guilt,
love with pain,
love with expectations.

I always forgot you.
That's just how I loved you.
Love with fear,
love with resentment,
love with avoidance and distance.
That's how I know nothing has changed.
You *still* make me feel guilty,
and I still forget you.

That's just how we love each other:
love forever intertwined with guilt,
and keeping our distance.
"I'm sorry."
"I've been busy."
"I love you."
"Do you remember…"
"I'm sorry."

Bloom

An ugly flower sits here,
an ugly, useless, barren bloom.
Untouched by nature, separate from its surrounding beauty.
Next to the still water, though surface be calm, all flowing life-giving
purity rages below.
Where trout and salmon play, protecting their young from bigger fish
and baited hook.

Sit brambles full of fruitful buds, soon to be plump and ripe to
nourish beast and bird.
Thistle, foxglove, coltsfoot and flax, made fertile by butterfly and bee,
dancing together in the air under sweeping, weeping willow trees.
Even flies, moving like stop-motion animation on stumps of trees,
feed on waste and spread disease.
Still they breed in thousands, their purpose instinctive and clear.

Nettles spring from thickets to catch and scratch their prey,
But even plants whose acid leaves sting, still flower and spread their
seed amongst the meadow.
In amongst the fecund nature sits this lonely ugly flower, pollen-free,
no petals bloom, no colour, all grey, barren, dusty plant.
Once young, filled with promise and life, giving joy and beauty.
Now stale and sterile, an intruder in nature's holy design.

Jealously it sits, fallaciously exists, no purpose only wasted potential,
wasted body, wasted life.
Nearby oak trees emerge from soft earth, roots like steps reach to
fresh streams; flowing through ivy carpeted glades.
The warm afternoon sun shines down in patches through light
green leaves.
A young holly tree grows, leaves still soft, not yet hardened by time
and painful to touch.

Christmas Dinner

For weeks we fret, flap and worry some more,
we buy more than we can possibly store.
Dad insists on sprouts for himself alone,
the dog drools, dreaming of the turkey bone.

Sis' is on a vegetarian kick,
whingeing about tofu till we're all sick.
Days to go the dishwasher's exploded!
Mum's hit the roof, it's Dad that's overloaded.

The extended family's piling in,
Grandma's polished off the last of the gin.
Emergency chairs are round the table,
one leg's broke under poor cousin Mabel!

It's been weeks leading up of strife and stress,
many hours beforehand of noise and mess.
For one single hour of family peace,
enjoying together this lovely feast.

For meagre minutes we treasure this time,
of family, food, peace, love and red wine!
Knowing how lucky we are and how blessed,
and when it's all over, *now* we can rest!

Daffodil

The day I was a daffodil, you made my leaves from green crepe paper.
The day I was a daffodil, I rode on the spring float, and cried,
because an older boy had ripped off one of my leaves.

The day I was a daffodil, every other child on the float cried too,
because of me.
The day I was a daffodil, I wish I had known, how few days I would
have left...

To be a daffodil.

Mrs Cutting

My husband's grandmother,
ninety-Six on her last birthday.
Her face, beautiful with age,
a line for every laugh, smile, tear…
The face of a life well lived.

She tells the best stories,
about growing up in the North
and her life during the war.
Half a Guinness every day…
Says it was for the iron.

Teaching me how to knit,
with wry wit and a hit, every time I drop a stitch.
She makes the best chocolate cake
(My husband's childhood favourite)
and won't give up the recipe.

Enjoys animal documentaries,
feeds the birds from her windowsill.
On our last visit, told a story about a childhood neighbour,
whose mother "Made her living on her back, and was the only one in
   the village with a fur coat"…

And no knickers, presumably.

Christmas Eve 2017: Millennium Bridge, Newcastle-Upon-Tyne.

I saw you that day,
on the bridge.
I was just walking along,
wholly unprepared.
Pausing my chatter
to stop and be benevolent.
A fractured philanthropist.

That's when I saw you,
sitting on the bridge
… smoking,
gaunt.
Accepting money from strangers.
You took my money and shook my hand,
smiling…
Saying, "Nice to meet you."
No recognition on your face.

But I saw you… I only saw you.
The world went away just then,
the ground beneath my feet crumpled,
oxygen fled my lungs.
Somehow, I left the bridge…
Reached a bench,
before I fell apart.

I wonder if she saw my face?
Heard the catch in my throat?
Or my quickening breath?
Did she think I was strange?
That girl on the bridge…
Whose face I can't remember…
Because all I saw was you.

It's funny how grief can sneak up on you.
(It's also funny how people say, "It's funny" about things that really
aren't funny.)
Five years since you'd gone.
Last minute shopping,
and trying to be charitable,
brought it all back.
Like I had you back,
just for a second.

Then I lost you all over again,
right there on the bridge,
on Christmas Eve.

The Hills of Home

The hills of home how tall they rise, old as aeons and solid as stone.
Battered by every force of nature still they stand, unweathered,
   constant as time itself.
The mouse and the fox call them home, untouched by man's cruel
   hand.
Giving shelter to the smallest creature, who hides and plays amongst
   peaks and dales.

The impassable beauty all the year creates within me a feeling of rest,
nothing can change the hills of home; vast and huge they rise.
Purple heather adorns their breast like a cotton summer dress
and lush green moss spreads over their valleys, velvet curtains drawn
   on a winter's eve.

Gazing up at the creation of nature's awesome hand,
I am reminded of my happy insignificance.
How little my worries are to me now,
while beholding the beautiful hills of home.

Constant and unchanging, unlike our mortal messy lives.
Boundless as the clouds, driving through the hills of home lifts my
   spirits and calms my soul.
For it seems to me that I am naught, here for just the shortest time.
A blink of an eye, in the lives of the hills of home.

Post-Christmas Nausea & PCOS

What if I'm really *not* pregnant?
I've been feeling poorly lately...
That's the only thing that's differed,
from the same old, usual routine.
This is all old hat now...

I had a period, then sex.
On purpose,
lots of sex.
Like energizer bunnies...
Only obligatory.

Then lying on my back with my feet in the air.
Avoiding alcohol.
Pretending I'm not thinking about it...
ALL THE TIME.

I've had enough of this merry-go-round now.
I've seen and done all this before,
look, there's that same tree again!
Except... This time...
There's nausea.

Maybe it's just Christmas...
(Don't think about it.)
I've eaten too much...
(Don't get excited.)
Nora's been going around...
(Don't let yourself believe.)
It could be anything...
(Don't get your hopes up.)

But what if?
I imagine that second blue line...
It happens to people all the time,
so why not me?
Oops, there go my hopes again...

Floating off up without me.

It's been four years of this shit now.
Four years of waiting.
Four years and counting...
Four years and nothing.
I told him about it...
That was stupid.

He tries, bless him.
But I'm in this on my own,
at least that's how it feels...
When he does his 'supportive husband' thing.

He says:
"Don't think about it."
(Yea, only when my brain's on.)
"It's too soon for morning sickness."
(Oh I'm so sorry, I missed your graduation, Dr.)
"Even if you're not, we haven't lost anything."
(....)
"We'll just keep trying!"
(I get up and put the kettle on.)

I don't think he realizes...
It's ALL I think about.
I want to spend tomorrow being violently ill,
at least that way I can keep hoping,
even though it hurts to.
Even though I'm terrified.

I remember the last time,
I cried at work.
The time before that,
I cried in the bathroom.
And the time before that...
It was a different bathroom.

I don't know if I can do this again.
Every time I *do* lose something.
Every single time...

A little something goes away…
A little bit of *hope*…
Every time.

"Please god" (lower case g)
I don't say that too often.
One more week to go,
until I can find out for sure…
Seven days, anything before that's too soon to tell.
I might drive myself insane.

Dreaming, hoping, wishing…
Are you in there, little foetus?
In nine months, PLEASE come greet us!
I won't buy you any Adidas, because it's a waste of money.
But I *will* love you more than life itself.

That's how I'll pass the time,
making up silly rhymes
(ripping off sitcoms),
and dreaming of a positive result.
I almost wish I was back at work!
At least it would take my mind off this.
(A bit.)

But what if?
This time…
One week and I'll know,
one more week…

Please.

*(Addendum, one week later):
It was negative.

What I Learned from Shakespeare

My formative years were spent in the company of many, but none so influential as the bard. At school I gave Shylock his pound of flesh and became complicit in Viola's deception. While others groaned upon hearing the news, inside I celebrated, at the thought of more time spent with the books in the running brooks.

Before I turned a teen, my home became the church. The building named for Shakespeare, but psalms rather than sonnets were what were spoken here. We prayed and sang and told old tales and laughed. The elders taught me much; Iago's all, some rise by sin, others by virtue fall.

From the judgement that filled those walls I learned to be respectful, quiet & not to argue... or to think. I learned that I was steeped in sin, I learned to feel guilt for things I could not control and to wear jumpers in summer as my body would cause others to fall. The sermons in the stones and the good in, not quite, everything.

At fifteen I went to work, at the Shakespeare Inn on Highgate. Years spent here, where the wine of life was drawn, taught me many things about life and love... and cleaning rooms. Time spent with fairies and young lovers – Helena was my favourite – a twin room, smaller and only single beds to make.

So many people came and went; four owners, three chefs, two managers and countless others through the doors. From these I learned good and ill, pain of loss, joy of gain and the bitterness of compromise. But its eternal summer shall not fade, and neither will the friends I made.

Mike*, always hidden behind heavy wood and dark ale, or in the flat adjacent, living his soap opera. He and a different woman each week made the beast with two backs. Once with my best friend, while I pretended not to care. Good Lord what fools these mortals be.

Of all I learned whilst working within its immortal walls, none so vital as this...

To thine own self be true, and don't piss off the people who serve the food!

Excited?

"Are you excited?" – It was the only thing we heard, from every friend and casual acquaintance.
"Are you excited?" – A hundred times a day. For months.

"Are you excited?"
"Yes! We cannot wait!" – It's the only acceptable response, and it was true, at first.

"Are you excited?"
"Yes, we cannot wait!" – But life is not that simple, and things could still go wrong.

"Are you excited?"
"Yes, we can't wait!" – But it's been a few weeks now, and the waiting is getting hard to take.

"Are you excited?"
"Yes, we can't wait." – But it's her birthday today and we're not with her, which makes me want to cry.

"Are you excited?"
"Yes. We can't wait." – But keeping up this level of excitement for so long is exhausting, and I'm starting to resent the question.

"Are you excited?"
"(Sigh)… Yes. We can't wait." – But my emotions are not that simple, there's also fear and guilt, anxiety and stress. Turns out adoption is complicated, so please stop asking me…

"Are you excited?"

Blowholes

Watching *Our Planet* on Netflix, feeling grateful for a glimpse into a
  world I might otherwise never see.
Watching in awe at the majesty of a mother blue whale and her calf,
  filmed from above by a drone.
Amazing modern technology,
bringing us something truly beautiful for once.

The sun sparkles off the clear blue ocean.
The whales, diving and re-surfacing, their huge tail fins
rising and falling from the surface of the glistening sea.
The tiny rainbows, dancing in the water sprays.
And the way the detail of the blowholes reminds me of a large
  vagina.

Don't Step on the Cracks

Children scream and play on cobbled streets,
jumping from stone to stone, trying to avoid the cracks.
Jump, wobble, balance, don't step on the cracks.
Children playing house, pretending to be grown.

She played these games too, once upon a time.
Today she plays like this:
jump, wobble, balance, don't step on the cracks.
Playing house, pretending to be grown.

At thirteen in the park, with vodka and friends, playing at being cool.
Eighteen in her own flat: work, dating and debt, playing house,
   pretending to be grown.
Ten years on, her wedding day: walked the aisle in someone else's
   dress, playing at being a bride.
Jump, wobble, balance, don't step on the cracks.

Her whole life just playing house, pretending to be grown.
Jump, wobble, balance, don't step on the cracks.
Thirty-two now and loving a child born to another, playing at being a
   mother.
Jump, wobble, balance, don't step on the cracks.

Happiness

Eating chocolate cake with a fork.
The sound of rain on the conservatory roof.
The moment just before falling asleep.
A churchyard in spring, carpeted with bluebells.
Rooftops blanketed in fresh, untouched snow.
Fish and chips at the seaside.
The serendipitous smell of walking past a florist.
Reading and listening to music at the same time.
The mating rituals of butterflies.
Kissing gates.
Parks on crisp autumnal days.
Spider's webs on dewy mornings.
The view from the Baltic observation deck.
Cutting into crusty bread.
Time spent with family...
Time spent with friends...
Time spent alone.
Falling autumn leaves.
People watching from coffee shop windows.
Travelling by train.
Daydreaming.
Birdsong.
A glass of white wine on a warm summer's eve.
Going out in a thunderstorm.
Starting on the first page of a new notebook.
(With perfect handwriting.)
Making someone laugh.
Taking the scenic route.
Open fires in winter.
Peppermint candy canes.
Listening to poetry recited by someone else.
Candlelight.
Inadvertently buying a Kit-Kat Chunky with chocolate all the way
  through.
Making love first thing in the morning.

Happiness 2 (in addendum)

All that stuff from the last one obviously, except I forgot about
  second-hand book shops, but nowadays there's also this:

Every time she laughs

(especially when I'm trying to be firm and she does her 'cheeky
  laugh'),

every time she smiles,

every time she says my name

(except maybe when she's screaming it at two a.m.),

her nose,

her eyes,

her legs,

her fingertips

(okay, so every single part of her),

every single time I say: "My daughter,"

her reaction when she sees cheese,

how much she loves her daddy,

the way she looks at me first thing in the morning,

every time she learns a new word,

her fascination with potatoes,

when she chases butterflies,

reading to her,

watching her play,

imagining all the things she could be.
(There's a lot.)

First Steps

I could not be the one to carry you inside or give life to you,
she could not be the one to carry you in her arms or guide you
  through.

I was not able to nourish your body from my own,
she won't be able to nourish your body while you grow.

I was not there to see your first breath,
she won't be there to see your first steps.

You share her blood, you grew in her tummy,
but I'll be the one you'll know as Mummy.

Sometimes I worry I've missed out on such a lot,
but it fails to compare to what she hasn't got.

Through her DNA you were given your eyes,
through our family you'll be given your ties.

She had your start and I'll get your rest,
from all of that, you'll find that you're blessed.

You have two mothers, never forget,
from each one of us, you've had our best.

Dancing to Silent Music

Laughter like ocean spray, lapping at the shore.
Unrestrained, filled with life and joy.

Hair warm like sun, soft as golden thread.
Draws my breath, like sleep and warmth and love.

She dances without music, her own rhythm, her own beat.
A secret song only she can hear.

The way she waves at no-one, the way she laughs at nothing.
An innocent mystery, free from inhibition.

Who was I before? Nothing much I can recall.
What purpose then to speak of?

Now I dance to silent music and wave when no-one's there.
Laughter, love and joy, free from inhibition.

Now that I am hers, I'm more than simply me.
Now and forevermore...

I am her mummy.

Understanding

When she grasps my hand in the dark,
the tears at one a.m. and the noise of the baby monitor.
Stooping hunchbacked over the side of the cot, back aching, legs
  straining.

When she won't let me leave, every time I move away, she screams
  for me again.
How eventually I just give up, lie down beside the cot.
My hand still holding hers through the bars, I fall asleep there.

The crick in my neck from the hard bedroom floor.
The sleep deprivation, the weariness all the next day.
The understanding that this is what it means to be her mother.

I *love* it.

SHORT STORIES

THE NECKLACE

"What's the matter, Celia?" Her father startled her, his concerned eyes glancing at her hands. C.C. looked down and realised that she was pulling at her fingers, a sure sign of anxiety. Trying to pull out words that didn't want to come, like a torturer attempting to force a confession. She put her hands in her lap and held them tight together.

"Nothing," she replied, not nearly as breezily as she was trying to sound, forcing her lips into a tight smile.

"You seem distracted, and you're very quiet. Are you sure you're alright?"

This was the moment: her parents were both here watching her expectantly, waiting for her to speak. It was now or never, they had given her an opening and she had to take it, she had to tell them. As the fear rose in her stomach, she felt hot and light-headed, but she opened her mouth and tried not to think too deeply as she forced out the words.

"There is something I need to talk to you about... And I just need you to remember that you love me, OK?"

"Would you look at that! It's absolutely disgusting!" Her mother's sudden holler pulled C.C. back to reality: had she said it? She looked at her parents, sat glaring angrily at the television. No, she hadn't, at least not out loud. Yet again she had begun to tell them, but they hadn't heard, because in a desperate and unconscious act of self-preservation her mouth had not allowed the words to escape. Instead keeping them safe inside where they couldn't wreak their terrible havoc. C.C. looked up at the TV, on the screen was an advert with a close-up image of a happy couple sharing a passionate, loving kiss. The couple were both men.

"What *is* the world coming to?" her mother ranted angrily. "Putting something like *that* on television when children can see it!"

"It's the PC brigade!" her dad replied with haughty distain. "They're trying to make it look *normal*!"

46

C.C.'s mother was nodding in agreement.

"I tell you," he continued, "there's going to be an awful lot of repentant people when Jesus returns!"

"The sooner the better!" her mother added as C.C. rose to leave the room. She reached the door just as her father replied with the obligatory "Amen!"

"Soon they'll be quoting Leviticus and speaking in tongues!" she thought to herself.

As she stood in the cold kitchen waiting for the kettle to boil, C.C. tried to imagine what her parent's reaction would be if she told them the truth. She thought about her childhood in this house, sat around the table in the mornings, eating breakfast while her mother prepared her lunch for the day. A kiss on the forehead, an acknowledgement of love and a wish for a good day as she had left for school every single morning.

She looked out of the window onto the large, immaculate back garden and remembered the fear and love in her father's eyes as he'd rushed to her side one sunny afternoon when she was twelve and lifted her, yowling, into his arms. Later that afternoon they'd returned from the hospital, her leg in a cast. Without a word to anyone her father had taken his toolbox from the shed and dismantled her trampoline; Like an act of vengeance, as though destroying the metal and fabric would somehow restore his daughter's broken bone.

She thought back to her first love, Peter Elphick, how devastated she had been when at fifteen he'd dumped her and told everyone in their form group that she was frigid. Because she wouldn't lose her virginity to him in the bathroom at Sophie Ellis' Halloween party. C.C. remembered how her mother had sat with her while she'd sobbed, not saying a word, then handed her a cup of hot chocolate and told her how much better off she would be without a wanker like that in her life. It was the first she had ever heard her mother swear, and the surprise of it distracted her so much that she'd burst out laughing.

C.C. smiled as she thought about it, then shivered. She couldn't imagine these kind and loving people who had guided her through life with warmth and wisdom being capable of turning their backs on her now. She couldn't imagine them disowning her, telling her that they could no longer accept her or that she was no longer welcome in their home. It seemed ridiculous to even contemplate, but she also knew how disappointed they'd be, how confused and appalled. They would never understand, and the best-case scenario would be that she spent the rest of her life as her family's shameful, secret disappointment.

Much worse than that, though. If her parents chose to, they could keep her from her little sister Florence; they might decide she was a corrupting or damaging influence. Ten-year-old Wren was C.C.'s favourite person in the world; because of their mother's unreliable fertility, they had been born eleven years apart. C.C. adored her little sister, with her impetuous nature and sarcastic wit. But she was young; she was still taking their parents' words at face value and had not yet begun to question their ideals. If she didn't want to lose her, C.C. had to keep quiet.

While she spent the rest of the day fulfilling her familial obligation, she wondered if she would ever be able to tell her family the truth, and what the alternative would be if she couldn't. Spending the rest of her life pretending to be someone else whenever she was around her family? Always having to be careful what she said and to whom? Living half a life, never being able to be honest about who she really was?

That night, as C.C. trudged up the three flights of stairs to her flat, she felt utterly dejected. She still hadn't been able to summon the courage to tell her parents the truth and instead she had spent the day smiling and being so careful not to rock the boat. Drained, she walked into her hallway and tossed her bag to the floor, collapsing like rubble onto her old grey sofa. C.C. let out a long, exhausted sigh. She'd spent her entire Sunday with her parents and all she had to look forward to now was work in the morning. Just as C.C. was contemplating giving up and going to bed she heard a knock at her front door. Hesitant because of the late hour, she opened the door, slowly at first, until she saw who was standing at the other side.

There in the dark hallway stood Jamie, who at that moment looked like the most beautiful thing C.C. had ever laid eyes on. "What are you doing here?" she asked breathlessly, and without waiting for an answer she stepped eagerly into a tender embrace.

Jamie smiled kindly, "I thought you might appreciate the company after today!"

"I really do!" C.C. replied wearily, running her fingers through Jamie's soft, chocolate brown hair. As they kissed, however, C.C. worried how Jamie would react upon hearing that she still hadn't told her parents about them.

C.C. pulled Jamie into the flat and absent-mindedly pushed the door closed after her. "I am *so* glad you're here!" she breathed as she wrapped her arms around her and kissed her passionately.

Jamie gently ran her fingers over C.C.'s cheek and through her hair, she pulled back slightly and asked: "So how did it go? Was it awful?" her voice full of compassion and concern.

"It was..." she began, trying to figure out the right way to tell her girlfriend that, for the third time, she had been unable to tell her family about their relationship. "I started to tell them and then –"

Jamie's brow furrowed. "What do you mean you started to tell them? Did you finish telling them?"

"Well I was trying to, but there –"

Anger flashed across Jamie's face, "Oh my God! You didn't tell them, did you?" Suddenly the anger on Jamie's face disappeared, and sorrow took its place. "Again... You *still* couldn't tell them about me..."

"Jamie I'm sorry! I tried, I really did, but you don't understand how difficult it is, they're so... close-minded!"

"This is the twenty-first century, C.C., and they're your parents, they'll just have to get over it!"

"That's easy for you to say! Your parents are left-wing hippies that support *everything* you do! You have no idea what it's like to be so scared that the people who are supposed to love you the most, are just going to reject you..." her voice began to crack, "just toss you out of their lives like rubbish!"

Jamie threw her arms up in the air and marched into the living room, slumping down on the couch in exasperation.

When C.C. entered the room, Jamie was sat with her head in her hands. She sat down next to her tentatively, "Jamie... I really am sorry. I'll tell them, I will!"

"I just don't know how much longer I can do this..." Jamie whispered sadly, "I love you, but I never wanted to be anyone's secret. I can't be your pretend roommate for the next fifty years!"

C.C. took hold of Jamie's hands. "That's not going to happen! I love you! I am going to tell my family about us, I swear!"

Jamie sighed, "You've said that before." She pulled her hands away from C.C.'s grasp. "Sometimes I just think... If your parents want you to be with a man so badly, why don't you just be with a man! It would make things easier for you..." she muttered bitterly.

"Jamie, that's not fair!" C.C. replied angrily. "Don't start with your gold-star lesbian bullshit! I didn't fall in love with you because you're a woman, I fell in love with you because you're you! And I'm not interested in being with anyone else, male or female. I don't blame you for being angry, but don't turn this into some kind of argument for lesbian versus bisexual."

"I'm sorry," Jamie replied somewhat insincerely. As they sat together in the silence that followed C.C. placed her hand gingerly onto Jamie's. When she didn't pull away, C.C. moved closer, she brushed Jamie's hair away from her face and began to gently kiss her cheek.

Jamie stayed still, she refused to move or even close her eyes, too stubborn to submit to C.C.'s touch.

C.C. moved her lips to Jamie's neck. Her lover smelled like honey and C.C. breathed her in, kissing the back of her neck softly. Despite herself Jamie's body began to unwind, and a soft murmur escaped her lips. C.C.'s hands quickly moved to Jamie's shoulders and she slipped off her jacket, Jamie turned sharply, their eyes met and for a moment C.C. was afraid, then Jamie kissed her.

They kissed with such need and hunger it was as though they had never kissed before and would never kiss again. They held on to each other like life preservers, all their love and need for one another spilling over, unsure and fearful of the future but both needing each other more than they ever had before. Tumbling desperately together, a line of clothes following them, they seemed suddenly to be in the bedroom, almost missing the bed as they fell together. C.C. ran her fingertips over Jamie's body, her delicate collarbone, soft breasts and firm nipples, across her stomach and along the rolling hills of her hips and thighs, learning every inch of her by heart. They made love for hours, gently and tenderly at times, frantic passion overwhelming them at others. As the sun began to rise, casting its pink glow across the room, they lay together shimmering with sweat and breathing deeply.

Jamie watched C.C. sleep peacefully in the morning light, tangled in bedclothes, her chest rising and falling with every soft breath that escaped her barely parted lips. She loved her, she loved everything about her. Her kindness, her generosity, her intelligence and her quirky sense of humour. Her freckles, the tiny turn up at the end of her nose, the way she laughed, and the way she cried, so bashfully, only allowing one tear to leave her eyes at a time. Her penchant for two a.m. Scrabble tournaments on the nights when her insomnia was bad. Her irrational fear of moths and her obsession with narwhals, the way she found it almost impossible to pass a bookshop without going in.

Jamie had never planned to fall for a bi woman; she had always thought that bisexuality was somewhat of a myth, a kink, a way for straight women to turn on straight men. That was until she had met

C.C. at Manchester Pride the previous year, who at that point had never been in a same-sex relationship before but had been so forthright about who she was!

"How do you know you're bi if you've never slept with a woman?" she had asked her. C.C. had replied indignantly: "How do you know you're not if you've never slept with a man?" then she'd laughed at the look on Jamie's face. She was so unapologetic about who she was, to everyone except herself anyway.

Seven months together and Jamie loved C.C. more than she'd ever loved anyone; she was the love of her life and she knew that C.C. felt the same way about her, it was in her eyes every time she looked at her. But the longer their relationship stayed a secret, the more Jamie felt like dirty laundry, as though she was being forced back into a closet full of darkness and shame.

They couldn't be affectionate toward each other in public, in case someone from C.C.'s church or a member of her family saw them. No photos of the two of them were ever allowed on Facebook and God forbid either of them changed their relationship status!

If they bumped into anyone C.C. knew, Jamie was introduced as "a friend from work" and as many times as C.C. promised and vowed that she would come out to her family, in her heart Jamie knew it wasn't going to happen. C.C.'s lies were so ingrained in her; hiding away had become her fortress, her protection, and Jamie knew that nothing could make her break free from it, not even her.

Jamie silently made her way out of the room, collecting her clothes as she went. In the living room she dressed quickly, and before she left, she wrote C.C. a letter. It contained no anger or bitterness, just love, a wish for it, a confession of it and the realisation that it just wasn't going to be enough. Then Jamie took the necklace she was wearing from around her neck. C.C. had given it to her the first time she'd said, "I love you." A delicate sterling silver chain with a heart charm, not a 'love' heart, but a tiny silver heart, with arteries, ventricles and an aorta cast in perfect detail. C.C. had said that Jamie literally had her heart, and that as long as Jamie had it, she didn't ever want it back. Jamie had worn it every day since, but now she placed it carefully on the coffee table with the letter, then she turned, walked quickly to the front door and left without a word.

When C.C. woke a little while later she could already feel the emptiness in the flat; it hung in the air like tension and almost hummed in her ears. She rose without a word and walked around, first out into the hall, then to the kitchen and finally the living room. She didn't call out for Jamie; she already knew she wasn't there. She saw the folded piece of white paper on her coffee table and as she moved closer, she spotted the necklace too.

Trembling, C.C. picked up the letter and began to read. Once she'd read it, she read it again, and again, concentrating on every word, as though she were trying to decipher some hidden meaning. Then she placed the letter back down and gently touched the necklace with her fingertips.

At first, she felt panic, her mind raced with a thousand thoughts. What could she do?

How could she convince Jamie to change her mind? She thought about calling her parents right then and telling them the truth, but she didn't; she just sat unable to move. Then a strange calm descended on her, she felt it moving over her like a mist. She knew that Jamie was right, she couldn't tell her family. She was too afraid of losing them, of losing their love and their approval but mostly of losing her little sister. She knew too that Jamie needed more; someone brave, who would stand up for their relationship and be the kind of woman Jamie deserved. In that moment C.C. understood that she couldn't be what Jamie needed, but Jamie was *all* that she needed. She'd never had such a connection with anyone, she would never love anyone the way she loved her...

Slowly and with salty tears rolling, one after another, down her cheeks C.C. stood and walked purposefully to the bathroom. She turned both taps to full, then walked to the cabinet and retrieved her bottle of sleeping pills. It was half full. By the time the water had reached the top of the bath, the bottle stood empty on the side, along with a long, sharp kitchen knife. Her hands no longer trembled as C.C. took a coral-coloured lipstick from her makeup bag and wrote five words on the bathroom mirror.

I'm Sorry, I Love You.

C.C. was calm as she stepped into the warm, clear water. As it began to turn red with her blood, like Moses' plague on the Nile, a thought drifted through C.C.'s clouding mind...

When they found her, they would find Jamie's letter and the neck-lace, and they would finally understand.

THE HEN NIGHT

When David and his wife Sophie announced to their friends and family that they were going to start trying for a baby, everyone was thrilled. Huge smiles and joyous exclamations were followed by bro hugs and pats on the back from the men, and queries about names and gender preferences from the women. No-one had told them the truth, not one of their loved ones (despite several of them knowing full well what they were about to go through) gave them the slightest warning about what the next few months would entail. But why would they? Humans as a species are conspiratorially secretive about the negative aspects of all stages of pre- and post-pregnancy; that is, after all, how the human race continues to survive.

The only person in either of their lives who said anything out of the ordinary was Sophie's mother, who upon hearing the news hugged her daughter excitedly and whispered in her ear: "Let's hope it doesn't work too quick, trying's the best bit!" Now, after almost eight months of trying, both David and Sophie understood with complete clarity how shockingly misleading that statement was. In fact, nothing could have been further from the truth. The reality of having sex in order to become pregnant was the most routine, obligatory, invasive, un-spontaneous and not-at-all-sexy experience of either of their lives. Gentle caresses and passionate exploration of each other's warm, salty skin for hours on end had given way to undressing themselves before enjoying ten minutes of closed-eyed, missionary quickies on pre-planned nights. And the tests, test after test! Ovulation tests, temperature tests and negative pregnancy test after negative pregnancy test.

But eight months was too soon to worry, or so everyone kept telling them...

Thursday November 30th, 2017, 17:35

Tired and fed up after a long day at work, and with the knowledge that another obligatory round of 'getting pregnant' was due that evening, David trudged up the flagstone path to his front door. He stepped inside; Sophie was home already but the house was quiet. David's first thought was that she'd gone to the shops, or round for coffee with the quirky cat fosterer next door. However, as he entered the living room and absent-mindedly tossed his leather satchel on the sofa, he turned to see his wife sat in the large, backed armchair at the other side of the room. Her head was in her hands and her shoulders were shaking with silent sobs, kneeling down beside her, David placed a caring hand on her knee. "Are you OK?" he asked, assuming that the stress of trying to get pregnant had gotten the better of her again.

At the touch of his hand Sophie jerked her leg away as though she were being electrocuted and David jumped back, startled. Without looking up, Sophie tossed a small, purple piece of square plastic onto the coffee table.

"What's that?" asked a cautious David.

"It's a condom!" Sophie barked from beneath her hands.

"A condom?"

Sophie looked up sharply, "You should know, it's yours!" She snapped angrily.

"Mine? What do you mean it's mine?"

"Just shut up!" Sophie shouted, "I found it in your jeans!"

David looked genuinely confused, unable to fathom why and how there could be a condom in his jeans.

"I don't understand!" David began earnestly, he frowned, his eyes darting back and forth as he attempted to understand what was happening.

"Which jeans?" he finally asked. Reaching down the side of her chair, Sophie lifted the balled up, dark denim trousers she had there and threw them, with surprising force, at her husband. He caught them just in time to keep from being hit in the face and shook them out, examining them closely.

"Where did you find these? I haven't even worn them in months."

"They were balled up under your side of the bed, I was putting them in the wash and I found the condom in the back pocket," Sophie sobbed, her head back in her hands.

"Sophie I haven't worn these jeans in months! I have no idea how a *condom* got in my pocket but it's not mine! I *promise!*"

"You've worn them since we started trying," Sophie replied quietly. "You must have, I did a clear-out back in July and I remember putting them back in your drawer."

They sat in pensive silence for a few minutes, both unsure of how to proceed. "Was it just once, or are you seeing someone else?" Sophie asked, trying hard to sound forceful and indignant, but her voice cracked as she spoke.

"Sophie!" cried David desperately, "That is not my condom! I have no idea how it got into my jeans pocket, but it's not mine!"

Sophie looked up, her eyes were blood-shot and puffy, she looked at her husband's fraught expression. "It's not your condom?"

"I swear it's not my condom!"

"How could it have gotten into your pocket?" She asked incredulously.

David sighed, "I don't know…" He sat down on the sofa and rubbed his forehead with his palm. "Maybe it's an old one, from before we started trying!"

"It can't be, I told you I washed those jeans four months ago!"

"Well I don't know!" David shouted, exasperated.

Sophie glared at him. "Don't get defensive with me! I'm not the one hiding condoms in my pockets!"

"I'm not hiding anything! I don't know how it got there, I swear!"

David stood and crossed the room. He picked up the prophylactic and held it between his fingers, studying it closely.

"What are you doing?" Sophie breathed impatiently.

"I don't know." David dropped the square, plastic wrapper, which flopped back onto the coffee table. He knelt down beside his wife and placed his hands lovingly over hers.

"I'm sorry," he said softly. Sophie looked up at him, "it must have been awful, finding *that*," he gestured to the condom lying imposingly on the table, "in my pocket, but I swear it's not mine. I'll swear on anything you like; I promise you it isn't mine!"

Sophie met his gaze without raising her head, she wanted to believe him, badly, but something was nagging at her. An uneasy feeling deep within her that, try as she might, she couldn't ignore.

Taking Sophie's silence as an acceptance of his declaration of innocence, David rose to make a cup of coffee. As he happily and absent-mindedly clattered about in the kitchen, Sophie sat and stared at the small piece of plastic on the tabletop which had the potential to destroy her marriage. Sophie loved her husband, she longed to set aside her niggling doubts and just choose to believe in him, but the sad truth was she'd had fears like this before.

The past few months things had changed in their marriage: her focus on becoming pregnant and the stress of this not happening had created tension between them. Sophie knew this, she'd been feeling it for weeks, but she didn't know how to fix it so instead she buried her head in the sand like an ostrich and continually told herself that everything would be OK once she got pregnant.

The truth was that it was all she could think about, her desperation to conceive was so much that Sophie was barely able to get through a conversation without mentioning conception or babies. Her favourited tabs on her laptop were all instructional websites, detailing various tips on the best ways to conceive. She couldn't pass a school or playground without imagining being there with her own imaginary child. Her obsession with getting pregnant had taken over her whole life, and as a result had created a wedge in her marriage.

David strolled back into the living room, placing a cup of milky coffee on the arm of Sophie's chair. He began to chatter inanely about his workday, obviously confident that the unpleasantness of earlier in the evening was forgotten. After a few minutes of chatting away and receiving no response, David looked up at his wife's faraway expression and realised she wasn't listening.

"Are you alright, love?"

Slowly, as if she were emerging from a coma, Sophie's head turned, and she met her husband's gaze. "Have you slept with someone else?" she asked calmly, without a hint of accusation or anger.

"For God sake, Sophie! I told you it's not my fucking condom! I don't know what else I can say to convince you!" David's voice became more high-pitched as he shouted, angrily protesting his innocence.

Sophie kept his gaze and without raising her voice she replied: "That's not what I asked. Have you cheated on me?"

David looked at her for a second before he began insisting again: "Sophie, I've never seen that before I swear! Please just –"

"Forget about the *fucking condom*," Sophie interrupted, venom beginning to seep into her voice. "Have you, or have you not, had sex with another woman?"

David looked at her, they sat, leaning forward slightly, maintaining eye contact but saying nothing for a several seconds. Until at last, still unable to speak, David's gaze fell to the floor…

Saturday July 22nd, 2017, 22:27

The table in the far corner of the busy cocktail bar erupted in drunken laughter. A tall, strikingly beautiful woman of about twenty-eight, dressed as a cowgirl, with dark eyes and dark hair and a sash which read 'Maid of Honour' draped across her curvy frame, was pushing a small box across the table toward her friend. The bride, identifiable by the cheap cotton veil stapled to the back of her fuchsia Stetson and the red L pinned to the back of her dress, looked down at the box in front of her. It was black, with purple text in the centre which read: 'Durex Intense'. The bride laughed nervously and asked: "What am I supposed to do with these?"

The rest of the hens laughed again, as the maid of honour gleefully explained the rules of the latest in a night full of games and challenges, directed at the excited soon-to-be bride.

"You have to get rid of all the condoms in the pack onto other people, without them knowing," she explained. "You can't hide them anywhere else, you have to hide them on people, but if anyone catches you, you have to do a shot!"

The group of hens whooped enthusiastically as the bride made her way around the crowded cocktail bar, dropping prophylactics into handbags and into hoods.

Then, discreetly sliding the last one into the back pocket of an unsuspecting man in dark blue denim jeans, who stood at the bar, complaining to his pretty young secretary about the inherent joylessness of trying for a baby.

ASCOT ST

(Inspired by the image 'Easington: August 1984'
by photographer Keith Pattison.)

She looked down from the window, the net curtain pulled behind her. All she could see of them from this angle was the tops of their helmets, a river of shiny plastic, hard and black. She couldn't see their faces, see the contempt in their eyes, but she could feel it. In the stillness, in the air as they stood, arms folded, waiting for the strikers to arrive.

The babe in her arms gurgled and whined, she bounced him on her hip as she watched, trapped. Trapped by red brick walls and single-glazed windows, trapped by sex and circumstance. Trapped by the past and the present and trapped by the future, but most of all trapped by the hundred-or-so men stood just outside her front door.

The police, in their smart four buttoned blazers and their hard, black helmets and transparent visors. Their oppressive occupation had lasted for weeks now with no signs of abating. Was it so wrong, to want a better life for your family? In this day, in this age, in this free country, was it so wrong to want a good life and fair pay and a home to grow old in?

They were soldiers, fighting a war on the side of goodness and right, of pride and honour. They would keep fighting, no matter how hard the batons or how empty their stomachs.

They could not give up, they could not give in.

THE LAST DAY

It was warm next to the fire; that helped. The stone under me was cold and I enjoyed the feeling of the cold stone and the hot fire. They kept offering me food: cheese, fish, biscuits, meat and milk. I remembered those things, the taste of them. I wanted to taste those things now, but my mouth was dry, and I couldn't make myself want to eat them. Moving was difficult, the thing on my neck was tight, it stopped me lifting my head, but the thing on my leg was worse, it got in the way. I could feel it all the time and when I tried to move it would catch my paw, like a cut or a cracked claw. I tried to shake it off, but it just stayed. I felt heavy when I tried to move and weak, as though I was carrying a heavy load, but my skin felt thinner, lighter, like there was less between it and my bones.

Something else was wrong, I felt it was wrong. I wanted to be away, in the dark where they couldn't see, but they wouldn't let me go. They kept bringing me back to the carpet, in the end I lay down, too tired to move anymore. That feeling, the weak, heavy feeling, was there all the time now, every time I tried to breathe. Like I had to lift my whole self just to take a breath. It had never felt like that before, that was how I knew it was wrong.

At least I was back from *that* place now, I was here where the fire was warm and I understood that I was home. I didn't like that other place, it was cold there and far too bright. Full of unfamiliar smells, they made me nervous, those smells. The humans there were strangers too; even though they knew my name I didn't recognise their scent, they were the ones who had put these things on me, I had been there for a long time and I had been afraid.

I was back now, though; I wasn't afraid now. I was with *my* humans, they sat with me by the fire and were kind to me. My favourite human brought water to wet my lips and my second human stroked me with the special glove. She always used that glove to groom me, and I enjoyed the feeling. I tried to roll, like usual, but I wasn't strong enough, my human lifted me over on to the rug, it was soft, and she stroked me again. My favourite human stroked my nose and he used soft words, he made me safe.

I didn't feel afraid now. I was sleepy, I felt warm fire and gentle strokes and soft words and love.

WANDERLUST

I smiled at the waiter as I sat fanning myself with the menu and waiting for my orange and lemon juice non-alcoholic cocktail. I had read about this place in a travel magazine back home, one of the few establishments in Marrakech ran by an English ex-pat, so I reasoned that if I was going to find work anywhere, here was my best option.

I sat and listened to the sounds of the marketplace coming to life all around me, as if the very stones were just waking up and beginning their morning routine. The ringing of bicycle bells as commuters wound their way through busy souks, the melodic whistle of snake charmers' pungis, the low din of interwoven voices from every corner of the square. Berber orange juice sellers and henna artists in niqabs calling to every passerby in the hopes of finding a potential customer.

Of all the places I'd travelled to so far, there was something about this place, Jemaa El-fna, I could sit and watch for hours, the melodrama of reality so far removed from my own sheltered understanding of life.

"Here you are, madame." The waiter, placing my drink in front of me, pulled me out of my reverie. "*Shukraan,*" I replied, Arabic for thank you, though probably pitifully mispronounced. "Excuse me," I called as he turned to walk away. He turned back and I asked: "Is the owner in today?"

He looked at me with irritable confusion. "You want owner?"

"Yes please."

"Something wrong?"

"Oh no! Not at all, I just wanted to ask about... something."

The waiter, saying nothing more, turned and walked away and I was left wondering whether I had made myself understood. I felt a little ill at ease, so rather than ask again I turned back to the square and continued to watch the scene unfold, periodically taking sips from my drink. Which, incidentally, was delicious.

After a few minutes I was approached by a short, white, grey-haired gentleman with dark, thick-rimmed spectacles, who introduced himself to me as the owner of the restaurant. I politely explained that I was travelling in Morocco and looking for some short-term work before I continued on to my next destination. The owner, who had by now pulled up a seat and joined me at my table, looked at me quizzically for a few moments. "How old are you?" he eventually asked.

"Twenty-six," I replied.

"It's not a good idea for a young woman to travel around alone in a country like this…" he murmured slowly.

"Well there's not much I can do about that now!" I smiled, he continued to look at me with a furrowed brow, obviously not appreciating my subtle attempt at humour. "I'm very capable, I assure you; I've made it this far, anyway!"

"Where have you travelled from?"

So I described in general terms my journey so far, setting off from England, hitchhiking around Ireland then flying to mainland Europe. Into Germany, busing down through France and Spain, then a ferry crossing from Gibraltar to Tangier, a train to Casablanca and finally arriving here in Marrakech.

The gentleman looked surprised and mildly impressed. "Did you travel all that way on your own?" he asked.

"Well, I met some other travellers in a hostel in Paris, I joined them for a while in France and Spain, but we parted ways in Madrid. They were going to Valencia whereas I had my heart set on Gibraltar."

"I see…" murmured the old man, pursing his lips in a way that suggested contemplation. He asked what kind of work I was looking for and I eagerly explained that I would do pretty much anything, but that I had experience tending bar, waitressing and cleaning.

When he asked how long I was planning on staying in Marrakech I replied that I wasn't sure, that it depended on how long it would take for me to raise the train fare for my next destination.

I was purposefully vague. I didn't want to tell him that I was basically stuck. That I had burned through my savings and that my credit card had been cancelled because I'd missed the last two payments. Nor did I tell him that my riad was only paid for through the week, and that if I didn't raise some cash soon I'd be sleeping rough with the hashish dealers in the park.

"Where are you going next?" he asked jovially, obviously now convinced of my virtue and capability.

"I'm not sure yet. Mali – I would like to see Timbuktu – but I may stop for a few days in Algeria along the way."

"Do you speak any French?"

"Oui monsieur, j'ai appris le français pendant mes années d'école."

The old man smiled at me, in the way you would if you were humouring a child, then said: "Okay, come back tonight at seven o'clock, I'll give you a trial. If you work out I'll pay you what I pay everyone else, 65dh per shift. Each shift is six hours and you keep whatever you make in tips, okay?"

I smiled and thanked the old man, then made my way slowly back to the riad.

After a few days working at the restaurant I was settling in well, although the fast-paced environment was unlike what I had experienced before. I had worked in a bar in Munich for a fortnight while I was exploring Germany, but that had been a much more relaxed atmosphere. I'd begun struggling with my energy levels and have since found that I now need to sleep during the day in order to keep going into the night. One night, whilst working in the kitchen, I happened to make an off-handed remark to another waitress about my concerns regarding paying for my accommodation. She immediately responded by offering me room and board in exchange for teaching her sister's boy to speak English.

So here we are, it's been a few weeks now and I have a nice routine here in Marrakech. I wake around 6am and go for an early morning walk around the neighbourhood, I usually buy an orange juice and some msemmen from a street vendor for breakfast and enjoy the calm of morning in the Medina. After a browse around the souks, or a stroll through the beautiful Koutoubia gardens (as yet I haven't been able to catch a glimpse inside the mosque). I usually head back to the modest home of the kind family who are sheltering me. I have a siesta in the early afternoons and wake in time to enjoy a meal with my adopted Moroccan family. After which I spend an hour attempting to explain to a churlish eight-year-old boy, who would much rather be outside playing with his friends, why the English language bothers with silent letters. I then head to the restaurant for six busy hours of waiting tables.

I have been in Marrakech for just over four weeks now: it's the longest amount of time I've spent in any place I've visited so far. While the heat can be difficult, the atmosphere is electrifying! The noise and smells of the markets and the square, the busyness of life all around me is truly indescribable, and the stereotype of Islamic hospitality is no misnomer: rarely have I come across a more friendly and welcoming people. But as much as I'm enjoying my time here, I am beginning to get that feeling of wanderlust again. The aim of this journey is to get as far as I can, to see as much as I can, while there's still time. I can't afford to spend too long in one place. My earnings from the restaurant are slowly accumulating; it shouldn't be too much longer before I have enough to continue on my journey.

Today is my day off. I have one a week, which I usually spend visiting some tourist attraction or other, as well as writing and sending my weekly letters to my father, my grandmother and my best friend Thomas and his partner back home. Today, though, I happened across a public telephone, and decided to give my father a call, something I hadn't done since France. He answered the phone in a pleasant manner, until he heard my voice, then his own changed. He was taciturn as I told him excitedly about my adventures and gave little more than grunts and one-word responses when I asked him about the goings on back home. I had called because I missed him, but after a few minutes I began to wish I'd phoned my grandmother or Thomas instead.

"Oh, and I'm teaching a little Moroccan boy to speak English!"

"I know, I got your postcard," my father replied coldly. I understood why he was so angry with me, even though neither of us had, or ever would, bring it up in conversation. He thought I was being irresponsible, and I was. Out of the blue I had walked out on my comfortable job as a legal secretary, on the rental contract on my flat, and on the man I had agreed to marry. I had used my savings to buy a plane ticket and had swanned off alone to journey around the world, with no plan, and only a vague idea of where I was going and how long I would be there. When he asked, I could give him no satisfactory answer as to my reasoning except to say: "If I don't do it now, I never will."

My father was angry because he believed I was running away from my responsibilities and obligations to pursue some childish fantasy of excitement and adventure. He thought I was throwing my life away; he didn't realise, he couldn't, because I hadn't told him, that I wasn't throwing it away. I was, in actuality, living it, while I still had the chance.

I put down the receiver and felt defeated. Speaking to my father had been a mistake. I was tired, my hip hurt where I had bumped it a few days previously, and the bruise was still not healing. I needed rest.

That was the moment I decided it was time for me to leave Marrakech and continue on with my journey.

That night, as the sun went down, I sat on the rooftop garden of my temporary home, listening to the stirring sound of the call to prayer being sent through the warm night air from every mosque in a two-mile radius. The song of this devout and humble city moved me every time I heard it, and now sat alone watching the sun set over this beautiful place, I realised I was crying. The phone call with my father had been bothering me all day; I longed to forget about it and move on, to push it out of my thoughts, but I couldn't. He had tainted this place for me, he had invaded my time here and now I would feel his oppressive presence until I moved on. It was heartbreaking. Marrakech had been my favourite place; I had felt at peace here, and now that peace was ruined.

That night I didn't sleep well, and what sleep I did have was filled with unsettling dreams. I dreamt of the wedding day I would never have, Thomas and my grandmother smiling and gushing with pride as I stood in a long, white, lace gown, waiting to walk down the aisle. The sun was bright, and the sound of birdsong filled the air as I began to walk down the grassy aisle, strewn either side with wildflowers. Then I saw him, standing waiting for me, his beautiful face smiling. I was smiling too, although I couldn't see myself, I felt nothing but warmth and happiness. I longed to reach him, to be with him, to hold him, then suddenly I found myself being pulled backwards. I reached for him and called his name, but he was too far away, I was pulled back faster and further until the image of my wedding was a tiny dot surrounded by darkness, and I was alone.

Later that night I dreamt of my mother. I was twelve years old again, and she was still alive. We sat together on the living room chair, as we so often did, looking at books, pictures and post cards of far off lands and strange cultures. My mother regaling me with stories and facts she'd read about them all, and as always, making hypothetical plans and promises about the adventures we would have in these places, when she was well again and when we had enough money. Twelve-year-old me sat, listening to the warm sound of her voice, smelling the sweet scent of her perfume and the smell of damp plaster from our old council house which filled my nostrils. Her favourite song 'Wild Horses' played on the record player; every bit of it was just as I remembered.

"Look at this! This is the first place we're going to go when I'm better!" She was pointing to a picture in a travel magazine, I stared up at her beautiful face, thin and tired but still smiling as she planned our imaginary adventure. "I've always wanted to visit Marrakech. Look at all those colours, doesn't it look amazing?"

The difference between the first dream and the last was that waking up from the first had been a relief, with the second dream, it was waking that was the nightmare.

That morning I woke earlier than usual and packed my suitcase. I wrote a letter to my hosts, thanking them for their hospitality and asking that they pass on my thanks to the owner of the restaurant, along with my apologies for having to leave so abruptly. I left quietly, being careful not to be heard. That was how I always left; I never have been good at goodbyes. I walked slowly, enjoying for the last time, the sights and smells of the Medina. Taking my last look at the souks, my last look at the square and my last walk through the gardens of the mosque. I boarded the bus to the station, where I purchased the farthest one-way ticket south-east that I could afford, out of Morocco, through Algeria and into Mali. I sat on the train, and as it slowly began to chug its way out of the station, I wished a silent farewell to Marrakech.

For the very last time.

THE VOW

Sybil waited anxiously outside the church. If she were to enter this side of the sepulchre, where the men worshipped separately, she would have to either keep her head down, be quiet and respectful and hope to be granted an audience, or instead use her station, hold her head high, be forceful and demand an audience using her position as gentry. The latter option, though probably more likely to work, carried some risk. Although she was indeed gentry, she was still a woman and was not permitted to be in this part of the church, let alone requesting unchaperoned audience with a nobleman and courtier.

Taking a deep breath, setting her shoulders back and looking straight ahead, Sybil walked with purpose into the nave, where there were stood several men communing together after the sermon. Sybil did not know the face of the man with whom she sought an audience; however, after a few moments she recognised his steward standing stridently before an archway. Ignoring the stares of the men about her, she strode up to the steward and met his gaze confidently.

"I require a private audience with Sir Richard," she declared, keeping her voice steady but low, so as not to elicit extra attention.

The steward, who could have been no more than seventeen, looked uncomfortable. "Please excuse me, my lady, whom should I say is making this request?"

"Miss Ferrer. We are engaged to be wed one fortnight hence, and I request an audience with the man who is to be my husband!" Sybil maintained her forthrightness and refused to yield to the steward's gaze.

After a few moments he bowed obediently, turned and walked away. Sybil could just see through the archway that he had stopped and was talking with another young man.

She stood and waited, feeling uncomfortable and conspicuous, but doing her best to hide it. Soon the other gentleman with whom the steward had spoken appeared through the archway. He was tall, with kind, blue eyes and light brown hair; he walked casually over to Sybil, a polite smile across his face.

"Miss Ferrer?" he asked. Sybil bowed her head and curtsied. "Sir Richard Bowes, how do you do, my lady?" Sir Richard introduced himself, bowing as he did so.

"How do you do, Sir Richard? I beg your pardon, but may we speak privately?"

Richard's brow furrowed, "You are unchaperoned, my lady. It would not be proper…"

"We are to be wed in two weeks, sir. You would deny audience to your future wife?" Sybil asked confidently.

Richard looked around. Upon seeing his steward distracted, he took Sybil's hand and led her quickly through the nave, under a stone staircase and into a small cloister. They stood before each other, alone, both feeling uncomfortable and nervous. They had never met before and for each this was the only time they had ever spent alone with someone of the opposite sex apart from parents and servants.

Sybil smiled uncomfortably. "It cheers me, sir, to know you are willing to break the rules."

"It does?"

"I do find sir, that occasionally, the rules require breaking."

Richard laughed and nodded. "You are right, my lady. I have, on occasion, found that to be the case!" After another few moments of awkward silence, Richard spoke again: "For what, my lady, did you wish to speak to me?"

"You are to be my husband, my lord, but we would otherwise not meet until our wedding day. I wished to meet with you sir, converse with you. I wished to know your face, before I walked down the aisle."

Richard smiled and nodded kindly. "As it has been some years since we have entered the seventeenth century, this way of doing things does seem a little old-fashioned, does it not?"

"I might go further, sir; I might even say backward!" replied Sybil curtly.

Richard paused and looked carefully at Sybil. "You do not wish to marry me, my lady?" he asked benignly.

Sybil thought for a moment before she replied. "I do not know you, sir, nor love you; and in truth, no, I do not wish to marry a stranger."

Richard nodded thoughtfully. Sybil suddenly worried she'd said too much. "Please do not take offence, my lord, I will be obedient to my father's wishes. I am fifteen, of good marriageable age and it is a good match, one which will benefit both our households greatly."

Richard smiled kindly. "Stay, my lady," he laughed, "I am as reticent to marry sight unseen as you."

Sybil was olive-skinned and slight with dark eyes and dark hair. Her mother, who had died during Sybil's infancy, had been half-Italian and as a result Sybil had an almost exotic appearance. She was the only daughter of Henry Ferrer, a prosperous landowner, and Richard, twenty-one, was the eldest son and heir of Lord Edward Bowes. He was also a knight in the court of Queen Elizabeth I. Both from York, their marriage had been arranged six weeks prior by their fathers. Sybil's father hoped to secure his family name and reputation amongst the landed gentry and in return the Bowes would increase their land and holdings, including some in the Americas, as well as receiving livestock and money from Sybil's dowry.

"Please excuse my forthrightness, sir," Sybil began, "but is there another... someone whom you would prefer to marry?"

Richard smiled and shook his head. "No, there is no one. I prefer to travel and am often away at court, so have little time for romance. I believe my father sought a marriage for me as he was beginning to doubt my ability to find one for myself!" he laughed.

Sybil smiled kindly, then shifted her gaze towards the ground, just for a moment. Richard noticed her downward glance. "But you, my lady? Have you someone whom you love?"

Sybil shifted uncomfortably again. "My apologies, Sir Richard, I did not wish to –"

"Please, my lady!" Richard interrupted. "I have no desire to infringe upon true love, you should marry the man you desire. If you wish me to speak to my father, I –"

"Oh, sir!" Sybil interjected in a panic. "I fear I have prejudiced this arrangement, that was not my intention! I very much desire for our marriage to go ahead, for the benefit of both our households. And with the Lord's help I will endeavour to be a virtuous and obedient wife!"

"I have no doubt, my lady, but what of your love?"

Sybil's gaze fell. "It is true, there is someone whom I love. Our courtship has been a secret these past five months..."

"You do not wish to marry this gentleman?"

"What I wish is irrelevant, my lord, marriage would be impossible... My... they... are of a lower station."

Richard nodded sympathetically. "Do not fear, my lady; our marriage will go ahead as planned, as long as that is what you wish...?"

Sybil smiled and exhaled, relieved that she had not inadvertently ruined her family's prospects. "It is, sir, thank you!"

"Miss Ferrer, whilst I am sympathetic to your predicament, I am concerned... I do not wish for gossip or scandal..."

"Fear not, my lord, I can assure you of my virtue, and my entanglement will no longer be an issue once we wed. I will be ending my liaison this very evening."

Having discussed the finer points of their arrangement, Sybil and Richard sat in the cloister for almost an hour more, getting to know one another. They discussed their favourite literature, poetry, songs and pastimes. Richard spoke of his love for travel, Sybil of her penchant for needlework and her love of music – she played the cornamuse. They discovered a shared interest in the works of Shakespeare and John Donne as well as a mutual passion for horse-riding.

When they left, having made plans to ride together two days hence, chaperoned of course, they were on friendly first name terms. Richard was pleased that his bride was intelligent, attractive, interesting and honest, and he was confident that given time, their mutual respect could grow into friendship and even love. Sybil was relieved that the man to whom she would be bound for life seemed honourable, learned but most importantly, kind.

* * *

Nine days later, just five days before she was due to wed, Sybil was sat in the barn reading. She preferred the solitude and quiet of the barn to her father's cottage, which was dark and usually noisy and busy with people. A shadow fell across the page suddenly and Sybil looked up, stood in the barn doorway blocking the light. Sybil recognised the silhouette of Arietta, their young scullery maid. This was the person whom Sybil had been illicitly courting for the past several months and from whom Sybil had, despite her efforts, been unable to disentangle herself. For though she was afraid of the scandal and damage to hers and her family's reputation should they be discovered, Sybil was deeply in love.

Arietta was young and fair. The muck and harshness of life as a scullery maid had not diminished her beauty; long, ash-blonde hair reached to her thighs, her bright green eyes sparkled like emeralds and a freckle for each of her sixteen years adorned the pale, porcelain skin of her face. As well as being beautiful Arietta was also brave: Sybil's love for her was returned in equal measure and Arietta never hesitated to steal away into secluded areas, to spend time with the woman she loved. Unlike Sybil, Arietta never seemed to feel any fear or concern about being caught, in spite of having just as much to lose: her shelter, employment and even her freedom were at stake if she were ever to be found out.

Both women were at great peril if caught. Tribadism was punishable by public flogging, or as much as three years' imprisonment and while each of them knew this, both felt their love so strongly that it seemed worth the risk. Sybil understood, however, that their relationship could not last; she knew that to attempt to continue with their affair after she was married and out of her father's home would be to risk the reputation of not only herself and her father, but also of her new husband and his family as well. Her honour would not allow this, and so her love for Arietta was doomed to be one which would come to an unhappy end. Knowing this, Sybil had tried in vain to end the relationship that night after she had spoken to Sir Richard, and again several times since. Whenever she tried however, Arietta's kiss, her scent, her touch would inevitably overwhelm her and render her helpless and incapable of rational thought. So, Sybil told herself, she would take solace in her lover until the day she was to wed, and then on that day their entanglement would end, and they would not see each other again.

Leaning casually against the doorway of the barn, Arietta smiled wryly at Sybil. "What are you reading today, my lady?" she asked.

"Another Shakespeare, a comedy this time, *Twelfth Night.*"

Arietta walked into the barn and lay down next to Sybil, resting on her forearm. "Read it to me," she said.

Sybil smiled at her and began to read. This was one of their habits: when Arietta found a moment between her duties, they would sit together alone in the barn and Sybil would read to Arietta (who, having had not formal education, was illiterate). And afterwards, hidden amongst haystacks, they would make love. Not one of the other occupants of the house ever knew or suspected, since the only ones privy to the young women's dalliances were the animals in the barn.

On this particular day Sir Richard Bowes, having found himself restless and in want of company and distraction, had rode up to the house to enquire whether his future bride would be agreeable to a ride. They had by now gone horseback riding together three times already. The master of the house, Sybil's father, agreed to send his manservant as chaperone and advised Sir Richard that his daughter could be found reading in the barn, as was her habit. Richard alighted his horse, which he led around the cottage, past the servant's quarters and over to the barn. It was a warm but windy day, and the wind blew against the sides of the barn, so that neither Sybil nor Arietta heard Sir Richard or his horse approach.

And since they were distracted, neither of them saw him either, standing just inside the entrance to the barn.

There he stood in shock for several seconds watching his betrothed in the arms of another woman, before getting back on his horse and riding away.

Later that evening, Sybil sat at dinner with her father, served by the kitchen maid and her apprentice, Arietta.

"Did you enjoy your ride earlier?" Henry, Sybil's father, asked her.

"I have not been riding today father," Sybil replied curiously,

"Your fiancé came this afternoon while you were reading and requested you ride with him. I sent him to find you: did he not?"

Arietta, who was carrying an empty metal jug back to the kitchen, suddenly dropped it and it clattered loudly on the flagstone floor.

Sybil's heart seemed to stop, and her stomach tightened. "Oh no, father, I left the barn to... to read in the kitchen, o-out of the wind." Sybil tripped over the words as dread began to fill her entire body.

"He must have missed you. No matter, I'm sure he will visit again before Sunday," Henry said cheerfully.

"I'm sure," Sybil murmured, feeling as though she were about to be sick.

Three days later Sybil had heard nothing from Richard, and she had been too afraid to attempt to talk to him herself. She had not slept, and every day she waited with dread for the inevitable moment her secret would be revealed. Every time someone spoke to her, she feared what they were about to tell her or accuse her of. Every time she turned a corner or entered a room, she expected to see guards waiting to arrest her. Arietta had tried to talk to her several times, but Sybil had refused and instead had avoided her.

Sybil was sat in her room, staring nervously out of the window, when her father entered suddenly. "Sybil, I am leaving for the home of the Bowes, to speak with Richard's father."

Sybil almost jumped from her seat "Why, Father?" she asked, startled.

Henry frowned. "You are to be wed in two days! The arrangements must be finalised and the terms of your dowry and such agreed upon..." he replied, bewildered by her confusion.

"When will you return?" Sybil asked.

"Tomorrow afternoon. Do not fear, my dear, it is a good match, everything will go smoothly!" Her father smiled.

Sybil loved her father dearly. He was a good and kind man and she was scared, more than anything else, of the thought of disappointing or hurting him. She longed to stop him from leaving, to beg him to cancel the arrangements in the hopes that Richard would say nothing, and they could continue with their lives as normal.

But she knew she could not do this, so instead she kissed her father goodbye and sat back at her windowsill. Where she stayed, refusing sleep or food despite the pleas of the household staff, waiting anxiously for her father to return, fearing he would be accompanied by guards.

The following afternoon Henry returned. From her seat at her bedroom window, Sybil saw his horse approaching from almost a mile away. Upon seeing that he returned alone without armed escort, she ran to greet him, still afraid of what he might say. When Sybil reached him, her father greeted her with a kind but weary smile.

"Father! How did the meeting go, what was said?" Sybil asked hurriedly,

"Child, let me dismount my horse!" her father chastised her. "I am tired and have had a long trip, the details of which I will discharge to you in time."

"Please father! Just tell me, did Richard have anything to say?" Sybil begged,

Henry sighed and thought for a moment, "Just one thing... It *was* somewhat unusual..." he began.

Sybil inhaled sharply,

"He requested an addendum to your dowry..." Henry went on absent-mindedly, as he unpacked his horse. "He wishes for you to bring with you to his home, one servant of your choosing from our house, who is to act as your chambermaid." Henry looked at Sybil irritably, "Of course he has many servants, any of whom could easily be put to this task, and for this *I* would have to lose a servant! But Sir Richard was quite insistent, and I could not refuse a condition to the marriage at this late stage." He sighed. "So, which of our household staff would you like to accompany you to your new home?"

Sybil smiled.

A GIRL'S REFLECTION

The long rocky path stretched out in front of her, and as she stared straight ahead at the pristine fields, rugby goals and the large brick building in the distance which the girl knew as home, she was suddenly aware of the stillness in the air. Nothing moved. No wind. No sound.

Then suddenly, a noise in the distance: a car was driving up the rocky path, and as it rounded the corner and appeared from behind the trees, she saw the familiar blue and yellow markings which told her it was a police car.

She watched it drive slowly up the long rocky path towards the sports club where her family lived and worked.

In that moment, without the clarity of articulate thought, she knew in her heart that something was wrong. Her mother had been ill before she had left that afternoon, and her father had been visibly concerned. It had worried her even then, and now, just a few short hours later, a police car was driving up to her house.

Almost in the same moment she dismissed the fear rising within her, her nine-year-old brain not equipped to deal with the reality she was facing.

Telling herself that the police had been called in response to the recent theft, she turned her back on the distant view of her home and ran back to her friends, who were playing nearby.

* * *

The following day after her impromptu sleepover, as the girl sat in the back of her father's car being driven home, she peppered him with questions. She was aware of the pensive silence, almost tangibly filling the car, but she was too nervous not to ask.

"How's Mum?"

"Actually, I need to talk to you about that when we get home…"

A pause.

"I saw a police car at the house yesterday. Was it about the stolen computers?"

Another pause.

"Yea."

After the journey home, which had seemed to take longer than ever before, the little nine-year-old girl walked slowly behind her father towards the white bungalow that housed her and her family. Now with the paralysing fear rising within her, that little three-bedroom bungalow, perched on the side of a rugby pitch, seemed huge and foreboding. Perhaps she sensed the new emptiness inside.

The nearer she got to entering that house, the more fear gripped her. And as her father stopped to unlock the front door, the silence was deafening.

"Dad," she said, unable to allow herself to enter that house, "where's Mum?"

Her father's gaze rested on her for a moment, before his eyes shifted toward the ground. "We need to talk about that, honey..." he replied quietly, opening the door.

She didn't move, frozen to the spot as the hot stale air from the open door suddenly hit her.

Her father looked at her, his eyes misting. And she knew, there was no question, so before he told her she had to say it, aloud, to know it was real.

"She's dead, isn't she?"

Her father looked sadly at her, a single tear escaping down his cheek as he silently nodded. "Yes."

Then the tears began to flow.

Six Years Later

A lot had happened in six years. She had moved to a whole new part of the country, started secondary school, and her father had re-married and had another child. She'd made lasting friendships and finally begun healing the wounds left by her mother's absence.

But now, lying in bed, darkness enveloped her, and with nothing there to distract her from the pain, so intense it was almost physically debilitating, she lay there, crying uncontrollably, not even fully sure why!

It had been six years since her mother's death and yet she still couldn't move on. So many feelings jostled inside her she barely knew which ones she recognised, and the uncontrollable crying just gave her a headache and confused her more.

Why did it still hurt so much? Why couldn't she just move on with her life?

"I'm sorry..." The words escaped her lips as she sobbed. They surprised her. Why was she sorry? She wasn't to blame! She wasn't aware of any feelings of guilt. But then her mouth repeated the words: "I'm sorry," and again, "I'm sorry, I'm sorry, I'm sorry." She sobbed over and over, and as she sobbed the words became unintelligible. But they didn't stop, and her lungs felt as though they could collapse at any moment.

After an unspecified amount of time, could have been hours or merely long minutes, crying and sobbing, "I'm sorry" over and over, she knew something was wrong. She couldn't stop, and although crying herself to sleep had become a nightly ritual, this felt different.

Still sobbing, she pulled herself out of bed and tiptoed her way across the hall to the bedroom of her father and his new wife. Quietly she knocked on the door and calling out for them she pushed their door open. Turning on the bedside lamp, her stepmother welcomed her inside. And the now fifteen-year-old girl (who still felt very much like that little nine-year-old, who lost her mummy all those years ago) started telling them of her pain, how she couldn't understand why it still hurt so much after all this time, or what she was sorry for?

She waited for the condescending request to return to bed and continue this self-pitying teenage griping tomorrow. But instead they listened and held her as she began to cry again. After a short time, her stepmother rose and brought the baby into the room with them to give him his night-time bottle. As the girl looked at her father, step-mother and new baby brother, she realised what she was sorry for, why she felt so guilty.

She was happy. Her mother was gone, and she was happy. Of course, one was not the cause of the other, but she believed, however justifiably, that her mother would have been distraught at the idea that her daughter would not continue to cry and lament endlessly after her death. Her mother had been unwell and had struggled with depression and alcoholism. As a result her self-esteem had been wrapped up in the love and dependence of her family, particularly her young daughter.

But now, after all this time she knew what it was that had been stopping her from moving forward, and she could finally begin to put the past behind her and accept that ultimately she deserved to be happy.

It would take time, but she would get there. Eventually.

My Mother & I: 1989

LIFE & OTHER WORKS OF FICTION

I

A rainy day at the end of summer, it was the first day of the rest of their lives and many other old clichés. Put simply, it was this: their meeting, their first 'Hello'.

That rainy day by the beach, when she lost her umbrella, she found a shelter much longer lasting.

He walked along the promenade, immediately she caught his eye, that bedraggled beautiful princess, chasing along the beach after her umbrella. Instinctively he offered his own, a gentleman to the core.

And that was how it began, as a gust of wind on a rainy day, taking her umbrella and in return offering: a meeting, a stranger, a chance.

Not love at first sight, as many might say, but rather an exchange of numbers to retrieve borrowed Items, this is the story that started it all.

A runaway umbrella brought them together.

That was the tale the grandchildren would know.

II

Love comes slow and quiet, not fireworks, or sonnets or long tangled words. It creeps in and takes you by surprise; at least that's how it was for him. It had been some time since the safe return of his umbrella, which he would now cherish forever as the instrument of his destiny.

That day had been like so many others, a meal together and then walking in the park.

As they walked along, her laughter and giddy joy at the beauty around them drew his heart toward hers. He watched her, transfixed, while she piled up mountains of fallen autumn leaves mere feet from the swing. Then as her long wavy hair, the colour of autumn itself, flowed behind her as she glided through the air, laughing as the carefully piled leaves flew in all directions.

So beautiful was her smile and her life, it came to him like a flood. As she swung back towards him, leaves in her hair, he caught her and twirled her around to face him. He gazed at her face, her warm smile and deep brown eyes. He knew in that moment that nothing in his life would ever be quite the same again.

Then he gave up his secret, his three-word sonnet, and as he said it, she smiled, the most beautiful yet, and they shared a kiss.

The kiss he would always feel on his lips, from then on, every time he closed his eyes.

III

Christmas had always been her favourite holiday, but this, the first ever spent with just those two, excited her more than usual. She had bought him an umbrella stand, amongst other things, a little joke in celebration of their meeting. She woke on Christmas morning at 6.45am, turned to rouse him, but found him gone. Her first instinct, that he had gone to sneak a look at Santa's generosity, but then she saw it: a note stuck to his pillow. "Come Downstairs" was its instruction.

She smiled and rose from the bed, eager to discover what lay in wait for her downstairs... A romantic Christmas morning breakfast with the man she loved...? A puppy?

She opened the bedroom door and stepped out into the corridor to a strange feeling underfoot. Looking down, she realized it was petals, a carpet of petals littered the corridor and stairs. She followed the trail to its end, quietly and slowly, her breath caught in her throat. The petals led her to the living room door, which stood slightly ajar and she could see a glow emanating from within.

She pushed the door open and saw the room, lit by the Christmas tree and candles, hundreds of candles covering every surface! And in the middle of the room, a box: a huge gift, beautifully wrapped in tissue paper with a tag that read another instruction: "Open Me." She looked around; he was nowhere to be seen, so she tiptoed toward the box, barely breathing for fear of waking in bed to find him snoring next to her. But as she reached out to touch the box, it did not disappear; she felt the ribbon between her fingers and pulled. The box fell open and revealed inside – another box, smaller but still beautifully wrapped. Again, inside that one, a box smaller still, and again and again until the floor was covered with tissue and ribbon and boxes of descending size.

Finally she held in her hand the smallest box, the last box, she looked around again, but still no one was there. Her heart stopping, her breath caught in her throat, she opened the last box, and inside she found: a folded piece of paper. Confused, she began to read its one last instruction... "Turn Around."

Her heart leaped to her mouth as she turned slowly: there, merely inches behind her, he was. Kneeling, holding in his hand a piece of jewellery more beautiful than anything she had ever seen. Overwhelmed as he began to recite the words she had dreamt of hearing her whole life, she began to cry, and as he slipped the ring onto her finger, they embraced. They sank to the floor, and there, amidst candles, and petals, and boxes, and ribbons, and a Christmas Tree, they made love.

IV

Finally, the day arrived. It's never as romantic as it is meant to be, more stressful, but there is usually a window, one small moment in the day when thoughts of ripped dresses, family feuds and dropping the cake all melt away. And in the future that window is what is remembered; all the rest is merely a blur.

For those two it was her entrance, each before in their allotted places, waiting.

As she stood behind those huge, white doors, nerves engulfed her. She stood in her beautiful white dress, arm in arm with the first man she had ever loved, about to be given to the last. And for his part, just as nervous, he stood, waiting, with the eyes of all he knew focused on him, as he stood fiddling with his buttonhole.

In that moment before the doors opened, they both wished exactly the same thing: that they could be alone with the only person who made them feel safe and comfortable. The one person they couldn't see, each other.

Then the doors opened, and she began her march. They both looked simultaneously, their eyes met and they smiled, their nerves evaporated. As she reached her beloved, and placed her hands in his, they knew without words, this was it. Then they spoke their promises to each other, meaning every word, they each knew that after today, after this moment, neither of them would ever need anything more ever again, because all they needed, they had. In each other.

V

Looking back on it, he didn't remember the fear, the screaming, or the panic; just what came next.

Eight months prior, they had watched hand in hand as that little blue line appeared and cried with joy. It seemed like mere moments had passed, and now it was time. It began on a Wednesday, at 2.17 in the morning: as he watched her scream and curse him for inflicting this pain on her, he held on tight to her hand and didn't let go, even when he thought his own would break.

As she screamed and howled, he was filled with terror. A million thoughts raced through his mind: "Surely it wasn't meant to hurt this much? Something must be wrong!"

But then the screaming stopped, and he stared, dazed, as the doctor gently placed this tiny person, into the cradled arms of the woman he loved. He stared at his wife, the girl he lent his umbrella to all those years ago; he stared at her, sweaty and smiling with her wet hair stuck to her face, holding this human that they had created together.

He was filled with more love and pride than he had ever known, or thought possible, and as he watched her, tears running down his cheeks, he realized she had never looked as beautiful as she did at that moment.

As a mother.

VI

People say many things about death; people say it is the only thing in the world that is assured, they say that it is just another part of life, but no matter what anyone says, it never makes it any easier to bare.

He had given her forty-six years, three children and a life full of happiness and love. As she stood to give his eulogy and began to speak of what he meant to her, his life and what kind of man he had been, all she could hold in her mind was his death, and the hole he had left in her heart.

She recalled sitting by his bedside that afternoon, just a few short days before. He had held her hand and told her it wouldn't be long, and they had talked lightly, about the weather and the garden, all the time ignoring the elephant in the room. But he had known, somehow in himself, he had felt death drawing closer. Then without fear or sadness, he looked at his wife; he saw her how he always had. With dignity and a warm loving smile, he squeezed her hand and said: "You can give me the umbrella back next time you see me." The same words he had said to her after the first time they met.

And then he was gone.

So as she stood, in front of their friends, their children and all of their family, she wondered how best to sum up her feelings. Was it better to have loved and lost? Did she know everything happened for a reason? No. Instead she said these words:

"Our life together wasn't all of the big memorable moments; it was the little ones we shared every day. Shopping together, doing chores, going for walks, or simply sitting together in the evenings, watching TV. It's the moments you don't take pictures of; those are the ones that are missed the most."

THE KEYNOTE SPEAKER

She stood confidently, a woman of obvious years and life; she spoke with command and carried herself with impressive self-possession. Physically I thought she struck the eye in the same way that down-town New Delhi might strike the eye of someone who had never stepped outside of rural Cornwall.

Her jacket and mid-calf length skirt were heavy-looking and very busy in pattern. They seemed to envelop her petite frame, and gave the impression that she'd wrapped herself up in a vintage carpet. When she stepped into better light it became apparent that her skirt and jacket did not match; in fact, they clashed considerably, as though competing for the attention of any and all eyes in the room. Both were red and heavily patterned but while the jacket was a darker orangey-red, with a pattern reminiscent of autumn leaves, the skirt was a brighter red, born from pink, with a pattern of white and black splashes across it like children's artwork.

Her hair was a natural-looking ash-blonde worn in a short bob, cut with military-style precision to rest along the bottom of her ear line, apart from a heavy and deliberate fringe across her eyebrows. Her black oval-framed spectacles, which seemed more affectation than necessity, brought to mind an ageing Yoko Ono. She wore them low on her nose, almost to the tip, so that when she looked out onto the gathered assembly, she did so not through her glasses but over them. And I wondered what effect or improvement they could possibly have on her vision. Later in the talk she took them off altogether and held them in her hand, gesticulating with them the way a weatherman does with his projector button.

Her shoes were sensible leather Dockers, flat but formal and tan in colour. They suited her and the matter-of-fact way she carried herself, even if they didn't quite work with the skirt. Her demeanour was calm but impassioned as she spoke with insight and authority about the vital subject that had brought all assembled before her: the mental health and well-being of children.

I could imagine a boardroom in some big city, charcoal-grey with a long chrome table in the centre. Seated around: several large white men in expensive tailored suits, full of self-regard and testosterone-fuelled entitlement. And this woman: stood at the head of the table dressed like a quirky lampshade, addressing those powerful men with authority and passion. Giving no quarter and pulling no punches.

I liked her immensely.

BANANA AND SALTED CARAMEL

"You know what'll happen if they catch you?" Blair admonished as Jude picked up her rucksack.

"I know," she replied resolutely, swinging the bag over her shoulder.

"Is it really worth it?" Blair pleaded "just for a –"

"How can *you* ask me that?" Jude cut him off. "For years they've held us back, kept us hungry and desperate. They took everything from us: our family, our dignity!"

"I know, I know! But Jude, eighteen stamps! That's weeks' worth of food! It's more than a tank full of fuel! It's keeping us warm through the winter!"

"They're my stamps, not yours!" Jude snapped defensively. "I've saved these myself and I never took anything from your supply!"

"I know, and look at you!" Blair cried. "You're wasting away! Living off one stamp a week for months!"

"I've managed," Jude muttered. "I'm going," she added, turning towards the door.

Blair reached out and took hold of Jude's arm. "Please!" he begged, making one last desperate attempt to reason with his little sister. "Don't do this! We'll figure out another way."

"There is no other way!" Jude replied, resolute. "They've taken everything from us – well, this is one thing I can take back. Just once, just so that I can say that those pigs couldn't get everything! They couldn't control *me*!"

Blair knew that Jude wouldn't be deterred; she'd been planning this for months. It didn't matter how dangerous it was, or how much Blair pleaded with her not to do it. And the truth was that Blair wanted to see his sister succeed, to fight back and to achieve something. Blair often wished that he was half as strong and brave as Jude was, that he could stand up and fight for what was right, but he couldn't, he was too tired and too beaten down. He let go of his sister's arm and watched in silence as she walked out of the house, begging a god he did not believe in that she would return.

Jude walked quickly through the streets. It was early dawn and the sun was just beginning to emerge over the horizon, casting a warm pink glow over the flats and tenements, which in the morning stillness were almost beautiful. In the distance a dog barked and was answered by another dog a little way off. As Jude approached the tube station, she pulled up her hood, aware of the security cameras watching from every corner.

Jude sat on the train, her hood up, leaning forward and staring straight ahead. She could feel eyes on her all the time, from the armed guards on the platforms, from the cameras, even from the posters displayed inside the train carriage. They were everywhere nowadays: shadowed figures of foreign-looking faces, usually middle-eastern, sometimes black or Indian, sometimes just eyes behind burqas, always with a vaguely sinister 'warning' beneath: "White Britons outnumbered in 10 years" or "The swarm on our streets". Jude could remember when she was young, when they were just people, ordinary people, just going about their ordinary lives. Now they were 'dangerous', they were 'swarming' and 'taking over'. But perhaps she was misremembering because of age and perspective: perhaps it had always been this way?

Jude found herself thinking about her mother. Once, when she had been around six, they had been on the bus, Jude couldn't remember why or to where. A group of four teenage boys had begun to catcall a woman in a niqab. They called her a "Paki" and a "letterbox" and asked her what she was hiding "under there". Jude could still remember the look on her mother's face: she'd never seen anything like it before and she never saw it again. It was like sadness, disgust and pure fury all at once. She looked at Jude and said, in a voice like stone: "Don't move!" Then she had stood up and, holding onto the seat bar for support, she positioned herself between the Muslim woman and the group of boys. Still with the same look on her face, she called to the driver that a group of teenagers were harassing another passenger. She still didn't move, even as the young men walked past her to leave the bus.

Then she went and sat down next to the woman. They were too far for Jude to hear what was being said but she saw her mother put an arm around the woman's shoulders.

After a few minutes her mother returned and sat back down next to her. "Are you OK?" she asked.

Jude nodded. "Why did they do that?" she asked after a few minutes of trying to comprehend the situation.

Her mother sighed. "I don't know baby, some people are just..." She trailed off. Then she seemed to gather strength, she sat up, turned and took her daughter by the shoulders. Looking her intensely in the eye, she said: "Some people are nasty, Judith; they're mean and they're nasty. Because they've been taught the wrong thing or because they're unhappy, or just because they enjoy being mean and nasty. Unfortunately, there are a lot of mean, nasty people out there, and we notice them more because they're usually shouting the loudest, or, working in politics. But there's always more good people, there are *always* more good people in the world than the bad ones. We just have to make sure we're one of the good ones!"

Jude snapped back to the present. The train was nearing her stop; she stood and headed to the door. As she exited the train, she kept her head low. It was still early and the station was almost empty, apart from the usual couple of guards and all the people sleeping rough. She walked briskly again, turning left out of the station. Right would have been quicker, but she needed to cover her tracks. She walked in a large, haphazard rectangle, weaving this way and that until she felt sure that her path would be too difficult to follow on security cameras. Then she ducked into a back alley, ripe with the scent of Biffa bins and stale urine. Shards of broken glass crunched under Jude's boots as she walked, slowly but purposefully, up to a large steel door. She exhaled slowly through her nose and knocked loudly. After a few moments a compartment in the door slid open and a voice said: "Name?"

"Jude," Jude replied nervously.

"Code word?" came the voice again.

"John Lennon."

The compartment slammed shut and Jude stood waiting anxiously in the alleyway. A few seconds later the sound of a steel bolt being slid across came from the other side of the door and it slowly began to open.

Once Jude was inside, the door closed behind her and she found herself stood in a small, grey, concrete hallway. A muscular, dark-skinned man, dressed all in black with long dreadlocks, had her turn out her pockets then took her rucksack and searched it. Next she was led into one of two small concrete rooms off to the right, and a white woman with bright blue hair, cut to just below her ears, instructed her to strip. She apologised and explained that it was necessary to protect their anonymity, then she performed a full cavity search.

Afterward while Jude dressed, the blue-haired woman, who had introduced herself as Lourdes, chatted to her breezily, apparently now satisfied with her lack of affiliation to the police.

"So, I noticed you have a lot of tokens. It must have taken you a long time to save up all those?"

Jude nodded. "A few months."

Lourdes raised her eyebrows. "Wow, you must be here for something big!"

Jude nodded again.

"You gonna pull a Guy Fawkes? Blow up parliament or something?"

"No," replied Jude flatly.

"Don't get me wrong," Lourdes added, "it wouldn't be a bad thing, it's just, you know… dangerous!"

"I'm not here for that. It's something else… a prohibited item."

Lourdes raised an eyebrow knowingly. "Oh! You're here for the speakeasy!"

"Yea," Jude nodded.

"Eighteen tokens? So either you're buying a round or you're here for the big ticket item?"

Jude nodded.

Once Jude was dressed and ready, Lourdes opened a door into a long corridor. "Have fun!" she smiled as Jude walked through.

Jude followed the dark corridor along to the top of a wrought iron staircase, black slatted steps with open risers. Jude hated these kinds of staircases: they made her think of hands, or claws, stretching through and grabbing her by the ankles. Nonetheless, she took a deep breath and stepped onto the first stair, then she began to descend, slowly at first, then faster. By the third flight of stairs she was jogging down. After another couple of flights she reached the bottom and walked along another short corridor until she reached a set of large blue double-doors. Pulling them open, she knew she had found what she had been looking for: 'The Cellar', an underground club where people could meet, away from the ever-watchful eye of the government and police.

It was amazing. Noise buzzed in Jude's ears; the atmosphere was electric. A huge warehouse, like another city centre beneath the existing city. Neon lighting in various colours illuminated the walls, classic reggae music wafted out of wall speakers as people from all walks of life milled around. No one shuffled or kept their head down, no one hid; hundreds of people of every creed free to exist without fear.

At the far left of the warehouse was a greasy spoon-style café, with mismatched tables and chairs upcycled from old beer barrels and delivery crates. The centre of The Cellar was open and full of pedestrian traffic, like the Spaghetti Junction for people, there seemed to be a flow to the foot traffic but there were no markings or cones, everyone just seemed to know which way to go. Jude decided the best thing to do would be to just dive in and go with the flow, walking amongst the throngs of people. She had a feeling not dissimilar to being herded like cattle, but it was fun. Eventually she emerged on the far side of the warehouse, which was full of stalls; it reminded Jude of the pictures of Berber markets she'd seen in travel magazines. Except these were not selling fruit, veg and spices. It was an underground market. Almost every illicit item was on sale here: drugs, weapons and hundreds of other contraband items including one stall selling old copies of banned books.

As Jude strolled through, she saw many books by authors she had loved growing up. Margaret Atwood, Maya Angelou, Ray Bradbury, Audre Lorde, Rebecca Traister, Kurt Vonnegut, Reni Eddo-Lodge… Then she spotted a copy of *The Conquest of Happiness* by Bertrand Russell. She grazed the cover with her fingertips. Jude could still remember the bright purple background and yellow bananas on the cover; it had been one of her father's favourites when she was a child. She could still see him, in his large, dusty, brown armchair, his reading glasses falling down the bridge of his nose, sipping coffee as he read.

Jude felt as though she could have been browsing any second-hand book shop on the high street and, for a second, she almost thought about buying it. But she knew that she couldn't afford to have something like that in her house, not just for her own safety, but her brother's too.

As Jude weaved through the stalls and past all the people milling around, she wondered what punishment just being in this place could elicit. All of these people were risking everything just to be here: if not their lives, then at least their freedom. A contemplative smile spread across Jude's lips as she thought about the bitter irony of it all.

They were risking their freedom, just to feel free.

Then she saw it, tucked away in the far corner, hidden amongst covered market stalls, a bright pink neon sign above which read: 'The Speakeasy'.

As she approached, she could see them all behind the counter: contraband, illegal for years, ever since the 'new' government had decided to classify them as a weapon. Jude hadn't seen one since she was a child. She took a deep breath: this was it, she'd come this far but if she was caught now all she would get would be some jail time. But *this*, if she did this, she would be risking everything. If she were caught, she would be deemed an enemy of the state, a traitor, and she would be executed. They may even try to go after Blair, try to prove he knew something. He could end up homeless or worse.

Jude stepped forward resolutely. This was her point of no return. They had taken everything from them, they had taken their family, their homes and their dignity. Forced them into tenements and slums, and that was if they were lucky. This was Jude's fight back, her first step towards resistance.

She stepped towards the counter and placed her eighteen hard-earned tokens on top of the glass. The man behind the counter glanced down at the tokens then back up at Jude with a raised eyebrow. He was tall and very slim; he had a large green mohawk which added to his stature, piercings in his nose and ears, and tattoos which covered his arms, visible because he wore a black leather waistcoat covered in safety pins, chains and zips. He looked to be in his fifties and had kind-looking blue eyes which looked out from under a heavy coat of black eyeliner.

"I take it you want the..." he nodded to a laminated picture on the wall above his head.

"The big ticket item," Jude replied, nodding.

The man leant forward expectantly and asked: "Will this item be... leaving the premises?" He raised an eyebrow knowingly at that last point.

Jude sat down on a tall stool at the counter and pulled off her rucksack. "No, that's OK, I'm going to drink it here."

The old punk looked shocked. "You're going to –"

"Drink it!" Jude confirmed.

"Eighteen tokens, and you're just going to drink it?"

Judith smiled broadly. "Yep."

The man smiled back. "Okay, then."

He turned to retrieve the item, then turned back around and held it in his hand as if displaying a priceless item of jewellery. A large, yellow cardboard fast food cup, with a clear plastic dome lid and a yellow and white striped straw coming out from the top.

The old punk placed it down on the counter with a flourish… "One large banana and salted-caramel milkshake, enjoy!"